Yasmin couldn't sleep. The rain woke her up.

1

Yasmin went downstairs.

"Oh help!" she said.

3

Mum and Dad came downstairs.

"Oh help!" said Dad.

The shop was flooded.

Everything was wet.

"What a mess!" said Yasmin.

The cloth was wet.

They took the cloth outside.

"Hang it up to dry," said Yasmin.

Everyone helped.

The sun came out.

"It looks lovely," said everyone.

"Let's have a party," said Yasmin.

Everyone was happy.